Mad About TRUCKS AND DIGGERS!

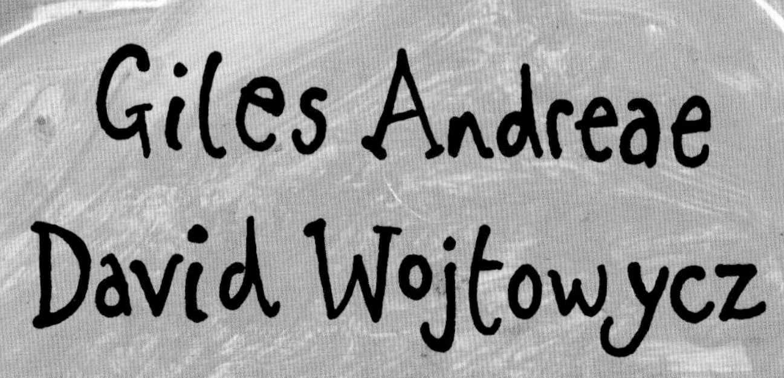

Giles Andreae
David Wojtowycz

Trucks come in all shapes and sizes
And are built to do all kinds of tasks.
Whenever their driver is ready
They'll take on whatever he asks.

Some of them help out the farmer,
Some carry big, heavy loads,
Some help to make our tall buildings
And some like to lay our long roads.

Of all the big trucks on these pages
Which do you think is most fun?
Let's look at them closely together
And see all the cool things they've done!

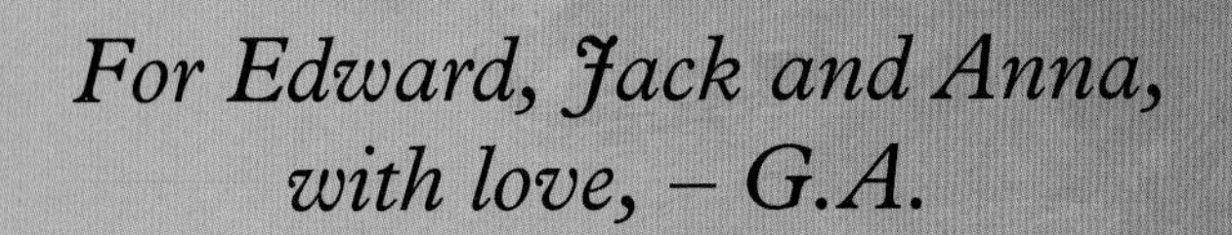

For Edward, Jack and Anna,
with love, – G.A.

From David to David – D. W.

ORCHARD BOOKS • First published in Great Britain in 2018
by The Watts Publishing Group • This edition first published in 2018
10 9 8 7 6 5 4 3 2 1
 • A CIP catalogue record for this book is available
from the British Library • HB ISBN 978 1 40833 964 0 • PB ISBN 978 1 40833 965 7
Printed and bound in China

MIX
Paper from
responsible sources
FSC® C104740

Orchard Books, an imprint of Hachette Children's Group, part of The Watts Publishing Group Limited
Carmelite House, 50 Victoria Embankment, London EC4Y 0DZ
An Hachette UK Company • www.hachette.co.uk • www.hachettechildrens.co.uk

MONSTER TRUCK

No other truck is as mighty as me
Just look at my giant great wheels!
I can spin myself round
Or leap right off the ground.
Woo-hoo, how fantastic that feels!

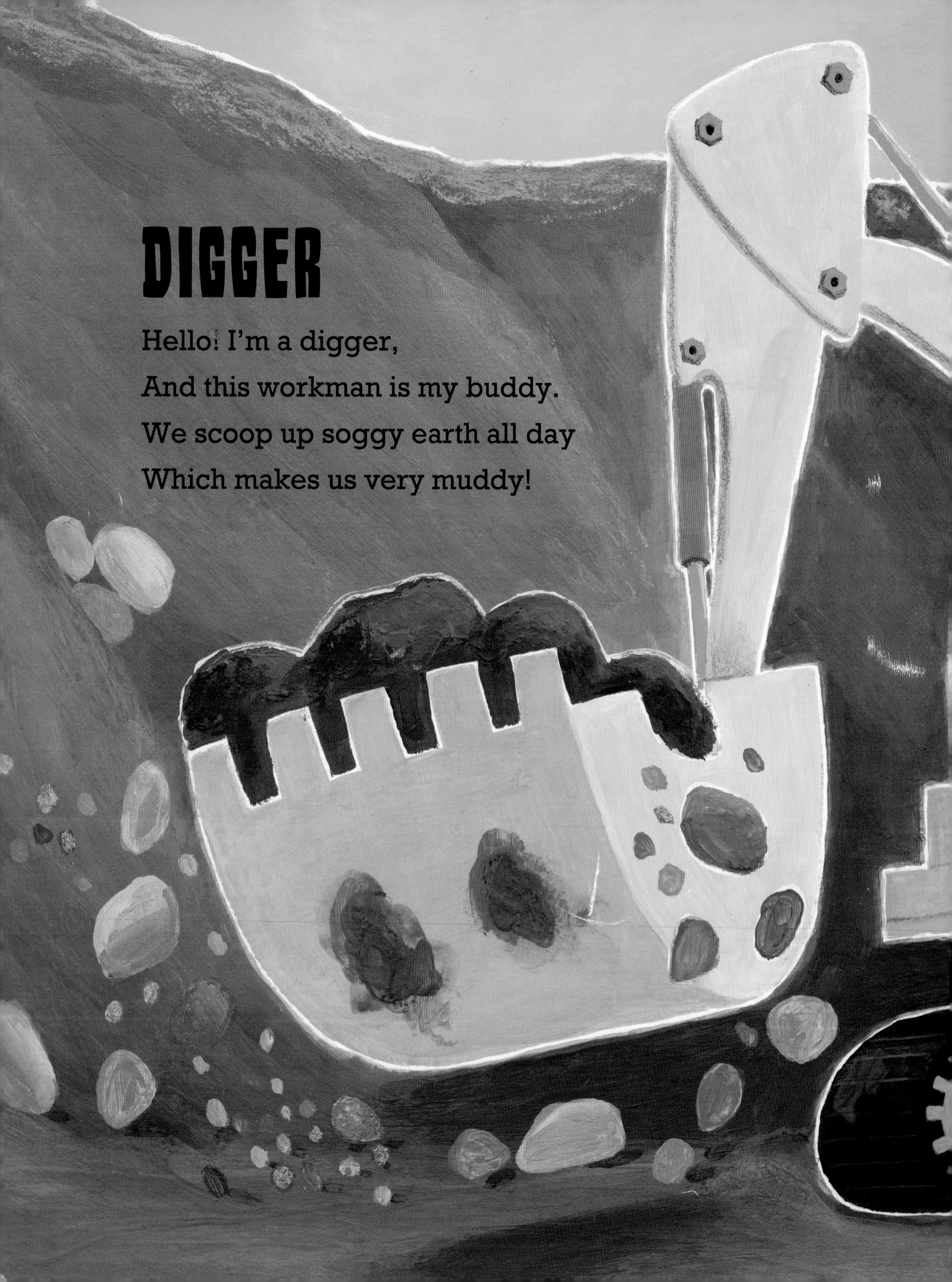

DIGGER

Hello! I'm a digger,
And this workman is my buddy.
We scoop up soggy earth all day
Which makes us very muddy!

STEAM ROLLER

I trundle along very slowly
And really love letting off steam.
I shake and I shudder
I jiggle and judder,
Yes, I am one NOISY machine!

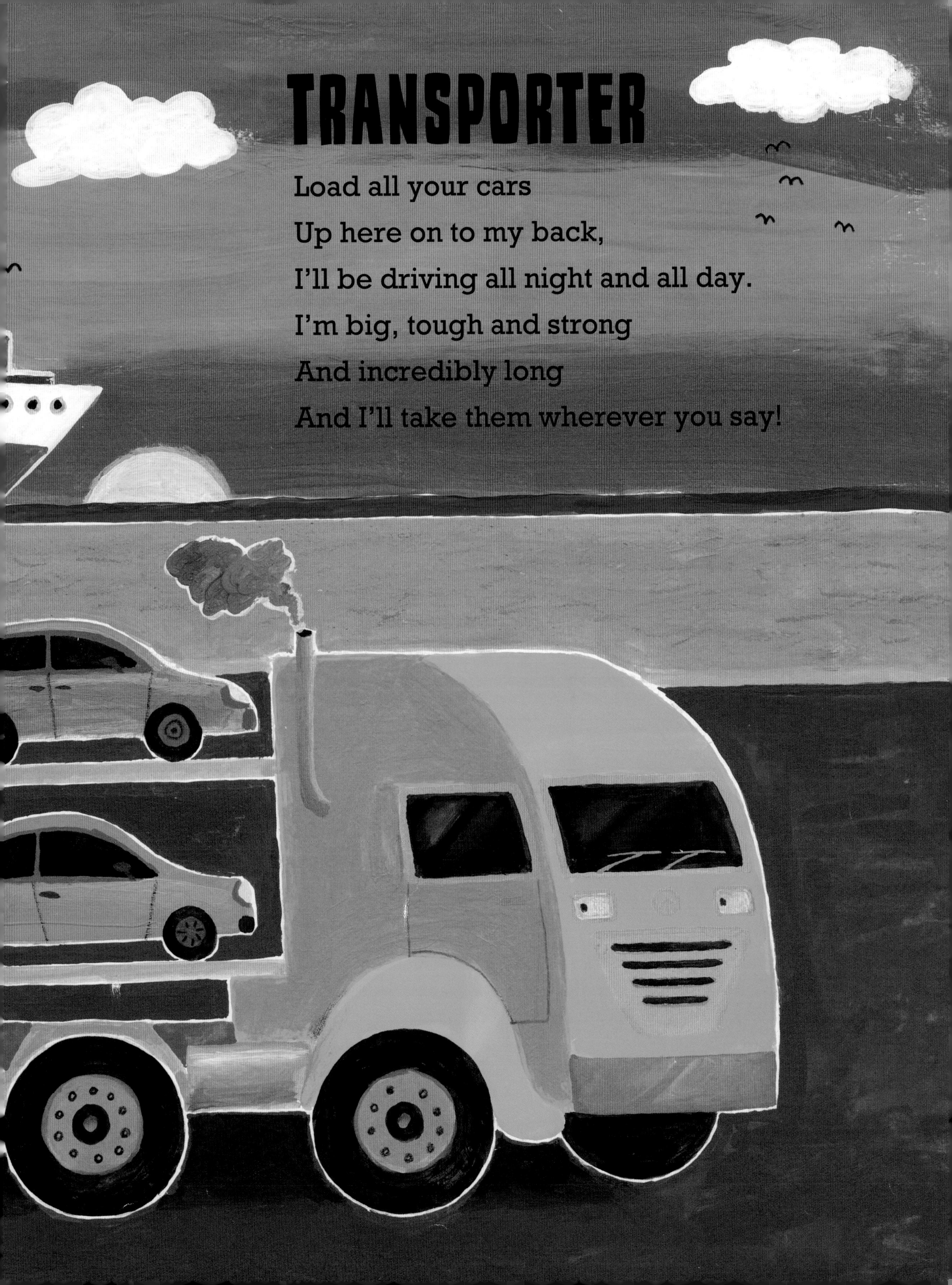

TRANSPORTER

Load all your cars
Up here on to my back,
I'll be driving all night and all day.
I'm big, tough and strong
And incredibly long
And I'll take them wherever you say!

CEMENT MIXER

I keep wet cement in my mixer
Which constantly churns it around.
Watch as it sloshes
And splishes and sploshes,
Until it sets hard on the ground.

DUMPER TRUCK

I am the giant great dumper,
I make a loud rumbling sound.
Just watch as I lift up my tipper
To dump loads of dirt on the ground!

RUBBISH TRUCK

You always know when I'm around,
I never need to tell you,
'cause when you're full of rotten food
Everyone can smell you!

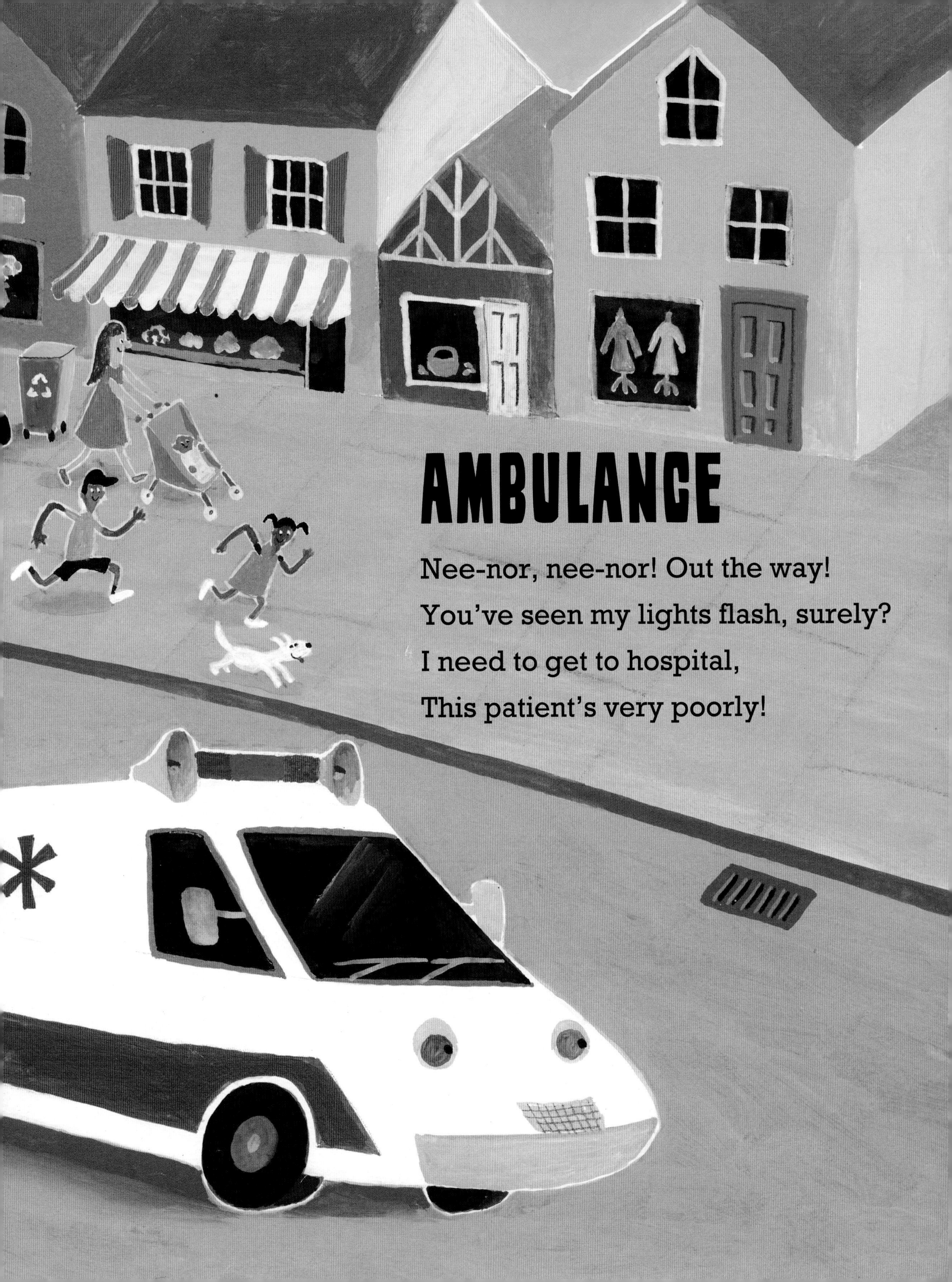

AMBULANCE

Nee-nor, nee-nor! Out the way!
You've seen my lights flash, surely?
I need to get to hospital,
This patient's very poorly!

CRANE

I reach to the tops of tall buildings,
A bit like a giant giraffe.
But please don't be naughty
And tickle my neck,
Or I'll probably fall down and laugh!

FIRE ENGINE

I've got ladders, I've got hoses
Oh, yes, look at me!
And my friends, the firefighters
Are as brave as brave can be!

TRACTOR

I'm the farmer's bestest friend,
We spend all day together.
She sits up here inside my cab
In every kind of weather!

Let's say goodbye to the trucks now,
I hope that you've had a good time.
Which do you think was your favourite?
Which one, I wonder, was mine.

Aren't there so many to choose from?
Tall ones and noisy ones too.
Yellow ones, blue ones and red ones,
And each with their own job to do.

Remember, each truck needs a driver,
And you're growing bigger each day,
So it probably won't be too long now
Until YOU can drive one – hooray!!